Eat It First, Ask Questions Later!

Based on the TV series *Rugrats*® created by Klasky/Csupo Inc.
and Paul Germain as seen on BBC tv

First published in Great Britain in 1999 by Simon & Schuster UK Ltd
Africa House, 64-78 Kingsway, London WC2B 6AH

A CIP catalogue for this book is available from the British Library

Manufactured in the United States of America

ISBN 0-671-02873-1

10 9 8 7 6 5 4 3 2 1

NICKELODEON®

RUGRATS™

Eat It First, Ask Questions Later!

by David Lewman

Table of Contents

Tommy Pickles

He's the bravest. And he's only one year old!

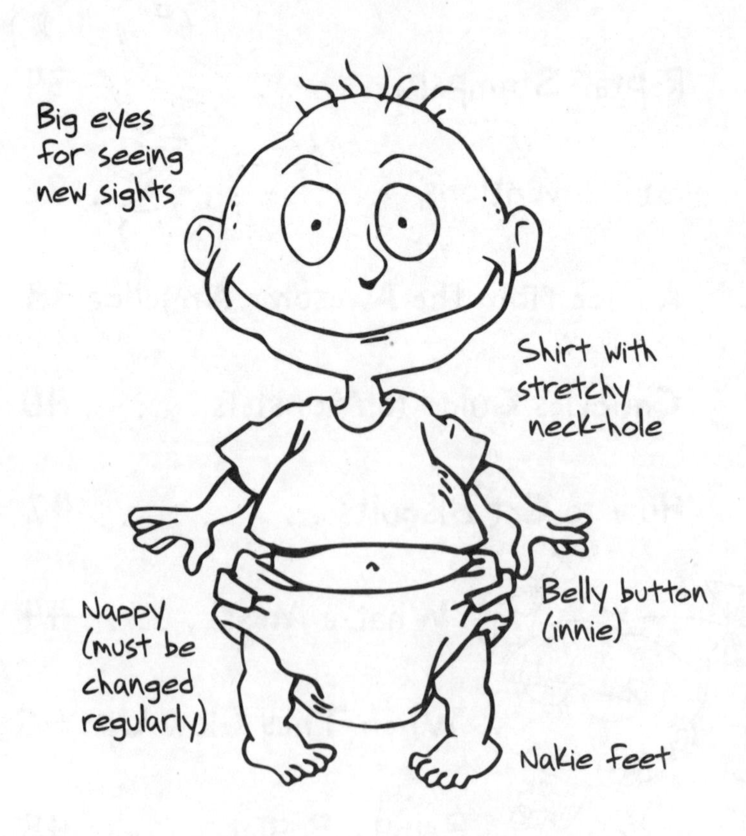

Chuckie Finster, Jr.

He's very careful. And he's Tommy's bestest friend.

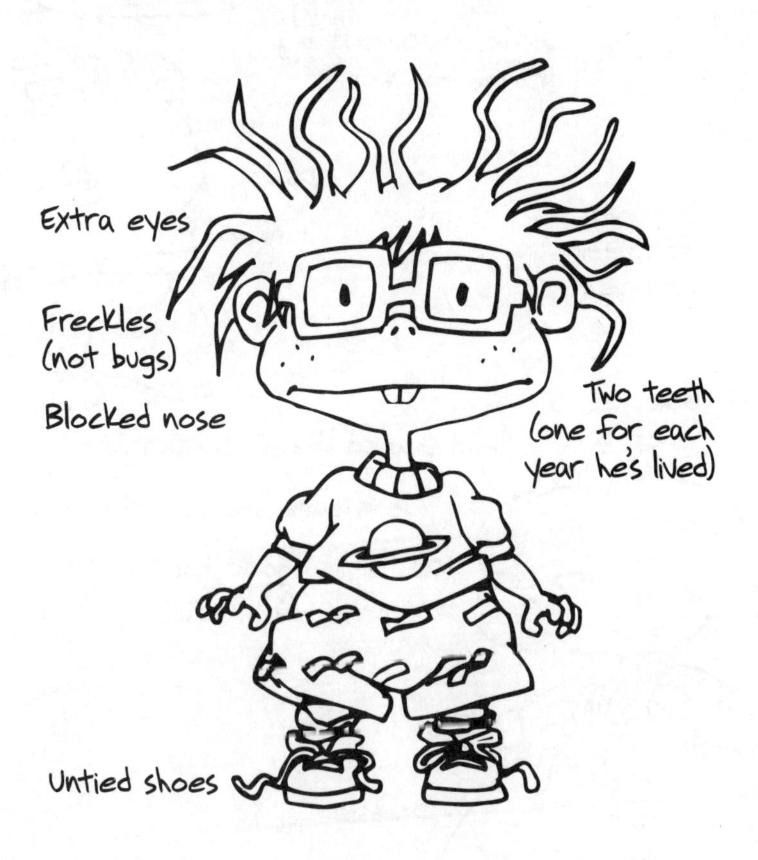

Phil DeVille
That's me! I look a lot like my sister. Mum says that's because we're twins!
Little mouth (but big enough for worms)
Ducky
Hankie
Bow
Head shaped like TV screen
Clean ears (she eats the wax)
Oval eyes (good for sneaky looks)
Dressie
Nappy
Lil DeVille
She's a twin—like me!

Angelica Pickles

She's a little bossy. Okay, she's VERY bossy. But then, she IS three!

Tommy in Charge

Whenever there's a problem, Tommy Knows what to do. I remember the time

- He got us all to be "nakie." That was fun!
- He took us on an "expulition" to the North Pole to see Father Christmas.
- We went into Grandpa Lou's room to face the big bed monster.
- He found a way to get out of the nursery.
- He took us to find the flusher to flush the giant potty (the grown-ups called it "the swimming pool").
- He told Angelica that we weren't going to make any more lemonade until she started sharing all the money.
- Tommy became Changing Boy to save the Mega-Hyper Heroes from Angelica.

- We went all over the place to find a moose.
- Tommy even went into the next yard, where the scary big dog lives, so he could get his ball back.

Life's a Mystery!

Life's a big mystery and it's up to us to solve it! Every day we find new mysteries. Here's what we've found out so far.

What's a "brizzerd"?
It doesn't mean the sky is falling. It just means it's snowing hard outside.

Where does light hide at night?
in the fridge, of course.

How can we get Reptar bars on Halloween?
By screaming!

What's a garage sale?
That's when you put all your old stuff out on the lawn for other grown-ups to take away. Then you can get new stuff. But we still don't know why other grown-ups take the old stuff!

What's a Lipschitz?
When Lipschitz came over, we thought maybe he was a mummy. But when he threw a tantrum, we knew he was a baby—just like us!

What's a dog broomer?
I worked it out: A dog broomer sweeps up dogs and takes them away.

How can Chuckie get unskunked?
By taking a bath in Grandma Minka's cold beet soup!

A View from the Top

You can tell who's who just by their hair. But if you're not sure, maybe these rhymes will help!

When Angelica saw my head she said,
"Look, a baby melonhead!"

My hair looks like a ball of flame.
Now maybe you can guess my name!

My hair has a little flip.
It looks a bit like a potato chip!

I tie my hair up with a bow.
What's my name? I think you know.

I've got a fringe and pigtails, too.
I've got much nicer hair than you.

My hair goes up and left and right.
In fact it's an amazing sight!

My hair is thick as any mop.
I just wish I had more on top.

Yummy and Yucky Food

The babies have eaten
some pretty disgusting things:

Worms (They called it "chocolate spaghetti")

Sand (Phil and Lil used it to make sandwiches)

Crayons (Chuckie ate two of Angelica's)

Dog food

Foam from Spike's
mouth

Stuff from belly button
(This was Lil's idea)

Leaves (Chuckie)

A spider (Phil)

Grasshopper juice (Lil)

Fluff from pockets (Phil)

But they try NEVER to eat
yucky carrots, peas,
or broccoli.

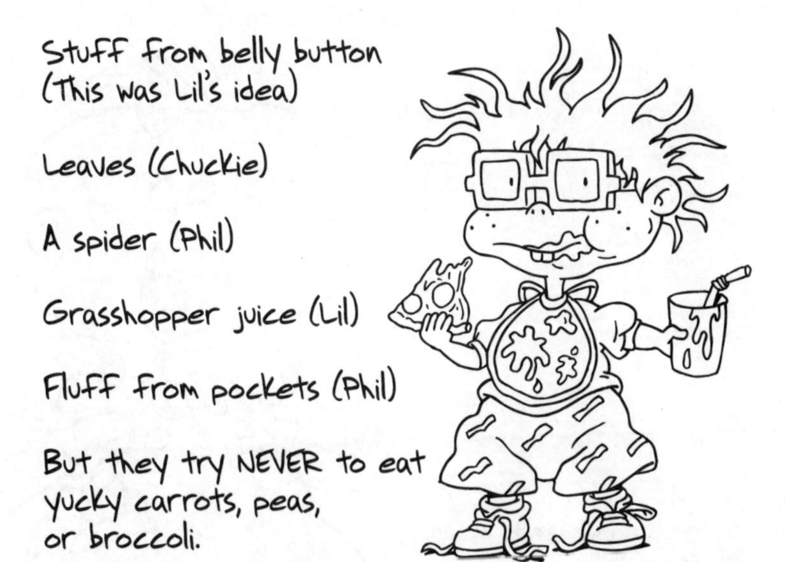

How to Tell Lil and Phil Apart

My babies look alike. But there's a way of telling who's who:

LIL
(Full name ends in "ian")
Bow in her hair
High chirpy voice
Wears a dressie
Pink shoes
Tried acting like Angelica, for one day.

PHIL
(Full name ends in "ip")
No bow
Low growly voice
Wears shorts
Blue shoes
Tried acting like Chuckie for one day

Words from the Wise

"A friend is a person who does whatever you say, no matter what, and doesn't make a big deal about it."
"Eat it first, ask questions later!"

Grandpa Lou's Tall Tales

Tommy's grandpa likes to talk about the past. But sometimes his stories are a little hard to believe.

GRANDPA: "When I was a sprout, if we wanted entertainment, we went out back and pulled up stumps."

TOMMY: "Was that for your stump collection?"

GRANDPA: "In my day we thought nothing of finding herds of elk living in our garage."

CHUCKIE: "I'm not sure what elks are, but I think I'm scared of them."

GRANDPA: "There we were, hunkered down in the shadow of an enormous bull moose, just a hair bigger than this house. The whole Pickles clan had moose for breakfast, lunch, and dinner for the remainder of the Great Depression."

PHIL: "I'd rather eat bugs than mooses."

GRANDPA: "When I was a sprout, I used to crawl through Ma's cactus garden huntin' for horned toads. And all I had on was my birthday suit!"

LIL: "Ouch!"

GRANDPA:
"Reminds me of
the fifteen years
I spent
prospectin' up in
the Yukon. One
night it got so
cold I had to
sleep under a
grizzly bear."
ANGELICA: "I can't BEAR
any more of these stories!"

It's Scary!

I'm scared of LOTS of things, like

- The dark
- Putting on my shoes (It's dark in there!)
- Getting an animal cracker (It's dark in the box, and I might get a scary tiger!)
- Green Jell-o (It looks like it's alive!)
- Bees
- The man on the porridge box
- Hubert, the big green monster (Grown-ups call Hubert a bin lorry.)
- Dust bunnies (Angelica told me about them.)
- The big monster dog next door
- But most scary of all are CLOWNS!

Angelica Knows it All

Those dumb babies will believe anything I say. They don't know I made it all up. Like the time I told them

- Ties keep the grown-ups' heads on.
- Two years ago, the sky fell, and it was the end of the world.
- If you swallow a watermelon seed, it'll grow inside you until it explodes.
- Chuckie is an alien from "outside space."
- If you catch the "chicken pops," you'll turn into a chicken.
- Tommy's new sister is coming in the post.

- The guy on the porridge box moved in next door.
- One time this kid got sucked down the plug hole.
- Phil and Lil's daddy's hair is a wig.

- Dust bunnies are big slimy horrible monster bunnies that snack on babies!

Inside Cynthia's Brain

Angelica's doll Cynthia has to put up with a lot. Ever wonder what she's thinking?

- "I hope my hair grows back someday."
- "I've been buried in sand so many times, I'm starting to grow a shell."
- "It's really dark inside a fish."
- "Luckily, my head pops back on."
- "The toilet is a lousy jacuzzi."
- "I want a REAL castle instead of one made out of blocks."
- "I'm all dolled up."
- "The worst way to travel? Inside Spike's mouth."
- "You know, that Reptar is really cute."
- "If only I could trade places with Angelica for just one day . . ."

Sniff On, Spike!

Spike loves to sniff around our house and yard. His nose is good for finding things like

Grandpa's room

Buried bones

Burned hamburgers

old milk

Hubert the Bin Lorry Monster

Spilled food

Dirty shoes

Wet squirrels

And . . . US!

Reptar Stomps!

Reptar likes to stomp. He can't help it—he's a dinosaur! Sometimes I wonder what it would be like for Reptar to stomp on

- A giant watermelon (SQUISH!)
- A train (he'd make it a "chew-chew" train)
- Big Ben
- Anybody who says Reptar isn't real
- A forest fire (he likes trees)
- The Empire State Building!

My fine son, Stu, spends his day inventing all kinds of things, including toys. Sometimes his inventions even work!

THE WHIRLYMOVER
Stu's very first invention, a breakthrough in children's riding devices.

PICKLES' BABY SUSPENDERS
Locks nappies on, so babies can't get naked.

A MECHANICAL DRAGON
It's huge! Every year, Stu builds a new one for the Renaissance Faire because it somehow gets beaten up.

THE STU PICKLES AUTO-SOFA
Automatically folds people in half.

BOPPO, THE TALKING KNOCK-DOWN CLOWN
Chuckie loved it, until he realised it was a clown.

QUACKAMATIC WEATHER VANE
Shaped like a duck, it tells you the temperature, the humidity, the barometric pressure—everything except which way the wind's blowing.

THE HOVERAMA
A flying toy with remote control made especially for Tommy's first birthday.

THE PICKLES MUMASSISTOR 5000
This was a gift for Didi one Mother's Day. With clap-on, clap-off controls, this contraption is supposed to do everything from vacuuming to making a Tofutti™ shake.

MR. FLUFFLES CLOWN LAMP
This one worked pretty well until Angelica broke it.

ANTI-GRAVITY PLAYPEN
And this one worked great until it fused all the electricity.

Advice from the Awesome Angelica

I know just how to get babies to listen to me and do things my way. So, LISTEN TO ME!

- Remind them that they're just dumb babies and you're a grown-up.
- Split them up by making them mad at each other.
- Bribe them with biscuits and Reptar Bars (then keep the goodies for yourself, of course).
- Tell them you're a real princess, so they have to do what you say.

(WARNING: Do not try Angelica's methods without permission from grown-ups!)

- Tell them you're going to dump buckets of sand on their heads if they don't do what you say.

Chuckie's Guide to Monsters

There's nothing to fear but monsters.
I know, 'cause I'm an expert.
And monsters are everywhere!

It's probably a monster if

- It moves in the dark
- It's breathing under your bed
- It growls—unless it's Spike
- Tommy wants to go look at it
- Angelica tells you it's not a monster (then it's definitely a monster!)
- It's as big as a house—unless it's a house

And if it's got scales, claws, horns, wings, four tails, and six heads, it's definitely a monster.

How to Get Biscuits

I love cookies! And I know just where and how you get them.

- Tell the grown-ups you need biscuits as medicine.
- Practice bowling, so you can win the Champion Chip (Cookie).
- Trade your Reptar Bars for biscuits.
- Make yourself invisible with vanishing cream so you can sneak into the kitchen.
- Say you need biscuits as "aspiration" for your painting. 
- Make your voice sound like a grown-up's with the Pickles Voice Frequency Modulator 5000, and order biscuits from Zippy's shop.
- Climb on top of each other and get biscuits from the kitchen counter.
- Move into a biscuit factory.
- Just ask your mummy or daddy to make you some!

What a Mess!

Sometimes we make a bit of a mess. But we're babies—and that's what babies do. There was the time when:

- We tried to get to the dog food on Chuckie's first birthday.
- Angelica made us spray a hose in the living room to make a swimming pool.

- Phil and Lil did a water ballet in the mud for the playground Olympics.
- Chuckie and Tommy used mustard to wash Henry the stuffed lion.
- We pulled all the toilet paper off the roll in the bathroom.
- We pushed all the rubbish out of the garage for Hubert the Bin Lorry Monster to eat.
- We fought over a bottle of chocolate milk--it spilled everywhere!
- We ate a chocolate pie and got it all over everything.
- We ate everything at the all-you-can-eat buffet in Las Vegas!

When They Grow Up

Someday all the babies will grow up. What will they become?

TOMMY

- An explorer
- A cowboy
- Or even the President!

CHUCKIE

- A safety inspector
- A hairdresser
- Or just like his dad

PHIL

- A taste-tester
- A bug collector
- Or the manager of the Minnesota Twins

LIL

- A bait shop owner
- A lawyer
- Or a hair bow manufacturer!

ANGELICA

- A prank shop owner
- A spoiled fruit inspector
- But probably a boss like her mummy

Being a Rugrat

The Five Worst Things

- Always being locked in the playpen
- Not being able to drive
- Having a stinky nappy and no one noticing
- Not being able to reach the biscuits on the kitchen counter
- Angelica

The Five Best Things

- Being able to easily crawl under furniture
- Riding Spike
- Small enough to sit on mums' and dads' laps
- No homework
- Everything's an adventure!